LITTLE PICTURES OF JAPAN

EDITED BY
OLIVE BEAUPRÉ MILLER
PICTURES BY
KATHARINE STURGES

PUBLISHERS
THE BOOK HOUSE FOR CHILDREN
CHICAGO

THIS collection has been made after careful study of the works of Basil Hall Chamberlain, Lafcadio Hearn, Curtis Page, Yone Noguchi, Arthur Waley, and Clara Walsh. The poems marked with a star are quoted directly from "A Year of Japanese Epigrams" by William N. Porter, and are used with the kind permission of the Oxford University Press.

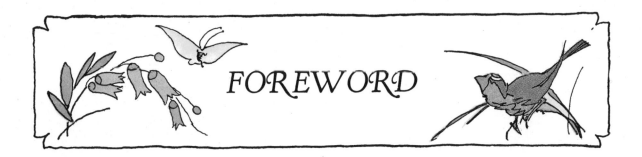

FOREWORD

FRIENDS of Moon and Winds—so were the Japanese poets called who wrote the tiny poems that comprise the greater part of this book. Dewdrops of smallest compass are they, yet mirroring in vivid flashes the whole of Japanese life. In few words of primitive, child-like simplicity these old sages sang, for the little hokku poems are gems of only three lines comprising no more than seventeen syllables, the tiniest poems in the world. These minute gems, however, usher one into that atmosphere of tender sympathy with all that has life, that world of benign serenity where dwelt the ancient poets of Japan. Cricket, butterfly, bee, and frog, stars, flowers, winds—these were the things of which they sang. What could be more simple or within the understanding of the smallest child? Yet here is real poetry, and not mere doggerel, the finest poetry of Japan. No one pretends that these beautiful little hokkus can be adequately translated into English. The Japanese themselves are rarely satisfied with any translation. Much of the beautiful terseness that suggests, rather than describes, and leaves so much to the fancy of the reader, is lost in translations. Yone Noguchi insists that translating Japanese hokkus is like taking down a beautiful cobweb and trying to set it up again in another place. Nevertheless, even when turned into English, there remains to the hokku a wealth of beauty and tenderness which is remarkably adapted to the understanding and interest of children.

With the inner rhythm of feeling, not necessarily the outward rhythm of sound, the hokku poets, in these little gem-like verses, sing the wordless song of the universe. Says one among them:

> "Eternity rolled in love,
> Bids the visible world to sing."

To all those whose hearts are sufficiently childlike to love simplicity and serenity, wonderment, adoration, and tenderness, this collection is dedicated.

*Baby's Hands

One chestnut, only one,
Is all his tiny hands can hold,
My little baby son.

Gomei

The Kite

The kite flies in the selfsame spot of sky
Where yesterday I saw it fly.   Buson

〖8〗

The Skyrockets

The voice of the rockets,
Then the flash!

Cool

O how cool,
Dangling one's legs
Over the verandah!

Azaleas

Under my balcony,
Among the rocks below,
Azaleas grow.

A Shower

Shower came;
In I came;
Blue sky came!

Izembō (d 1710)

The Rains of Spring

The rains of spring
Which hang to the branches
Of the green willow,
Look like pearls upon a string.

Lady Ise (about 1000 A.D.)

Sunset through a Shower

How cool the air!
And through a shower
The radiance of the setting sun.

Snail, Snail!

Snail, snail,
Put out your horns
For a little!
It rains and the wind is blowing,
So put out your horns,
Just for a little while!

The Snail Puts out his Horns

The snail puts out his horns, and see!
Eyes, like shining drops of dew,
Upon the ends has he!

Ransetsu (1654-1707)

Hurry! Hurry! Mr. Crow!

Hurry, hurry, tardy crow!
Your house is on fire! You're far too slow!
Hurry with water to throw upon it;
If you've no water, I'll give you some free;
If you've too much, give it to your child;
If you've no child, then give it back to me!

The Cuckoo

Although my house
Stands near the valley there,
Although my village
Has tall trees everywhere,
The cuckoo, herald of the spring,
Has not yet come to sing.
Hoping to hear
His voice so clear,
I go out to the gate
In the morning;
In the evening late
I cross the valley.
But, though I long,
Not even one song
Have I yet heard.

Hironaha (750 A.D.)

*Cloud Shadows

The clouds on spring winds borne,
Cast swiftly moving shadows o'er
The waving fields of corn.

Spring

When from her winter-prison
Spring comes forth,
In the morning
The white dew falls;
In the evening
The mists trail,
And in the valley of Hatsu-se
Beneath the twigs of the trees,
The nightingale sings.

The Spring Wind's Song

Today in silence I tramp along,
For ah, what hymn of mine
Could make such music as the spring wind's song?

Where do the Winds Live?

Where do the winds live, pray tell,—
The winds that scatter the spring flowers?
If I could find them, I'd scold them well!

Soft Winds

From the holy mountain
The winds blow softly, softly,—
Soyo-soyoto.

A House for a Frog

Come, little green frog, do!
I'll take some barley straw,
And make a house for you!

Chigetsū (A lady, 1634-1706)

A Sleeping Butterfly

Wake up! Wake up!
I'll make of thee my comrade,
Sleeping butterfly.

Bashō (1643-1694)

Butterfly Dreams

Even while it sleeps,
It dreams of play,
O, butterfly of the grass!

Dreams of Flowers

If butterflies could only speak,
What pretty dreams
We'd hear about the flowers!

Reikan

The Messenger of Spring

Were it not for the voice
Of the nightingale singing clear,
How would mountain villages,
Where snow is still unmelted,
Ever know that spring is here?

Nakatsukasa (about 900 A. D.)

O Keep the Nightingale

Around the plum flowers, pray,
Build a fence, so the nightingale
Cannot fly away.

Contrast

The nightingale's sweet song—
But Oh, alack! What a noise at the gate!
The bean-cake peddler comes bawling along!

Yaha (1663-1740)

Viewing Plum Blossoms

White blossoms of the plum and lo!
Five jinrickishas in a row!

*Plum Blossoms

Far across hill and dale
The blossoms of the plum have cast
A delicate pink veil.

Bashō

So sweet the plum trees smell!
Would that the brush that paints the flower
Could paint the scent as well.

I came to look, and lo,
The plum tree petals scatter down
A fall of purest snow.

Rankō (1728-99)

Chums

A shower in spring,
And there in lively talk,
A rain-coat and umbrella walk!

Buson

A Scurry

A sudden shower, and such a scurry,—
People thinking in a hurry
How to cover up their heads!

Otsūyū (1739)

Who Stole the Flowers?

Ha! the butterfly!
It is following the person
Who stole the flowers.

**Breezes*

When the spring breezes rise,
They play all sorts of merry games
With birds and butterflies.

Fluttering Butterflies

Though I should say
It does not seem to be a windy day,
Lo! fluttering of the butterflies.

A Pair of Butterflies

Dancing, dancing, there they go
Till they meet, and then heigho!
How still the pair!

Never in a Hurry

Ah, the butterfly!
Even when chased it never seems
In a hurry.

The Sad Fish Salesman

Alack, while others roam today
To see the cherries, I must stay
And sell my fish at home!

Cherry Blossoms in Sunset

Cherry blossoms in sunset light!
I lean my breast upon my staff and pause
To view the lovely sight.

Soa

〖31〗

O Spare the Blossoms!

O honorable slave boys
Of the Lord Chamberlain,
If you've hearts, I pray,
Spare your morning brooms this spring,—
Don't sweep those fallen petals away.

Minamoto no Kintada (about 900 A. D.)

Cherry Blossoms by an Empty House

The cherry blossoms
Of the empty house in the reeds
Must be very glad,
As they fall in the wind, that there's no one
For their falling to make sad.

Yekei Hoshi (about 990 A.D.)

【33】

No Place for the Sword

A sword!—
Why should one bring such a thing,
Who comes to view the flowers in spring?

Kyorai (1651-1704)

【34】

Hours Well Spent

Months and days I've wasted
　　Doing some useless thing,—
How few the hours that have been well spent,
　　Viewing the flowers in spring!

Fuijiwara no Okikaze (about 910 A. D.)

A Spring Day

'Tis the spring day,
With lovely far-away light;
　　Why must the flowers fall,
With hearts unquiet?

Kino Tomonori

Wisteria

Wisteria in bloom!
Above my lake it trails along.
When will the cuckoo come,
And make the garden musical
With his first song?

Hitomaro (about 700 A. D.)

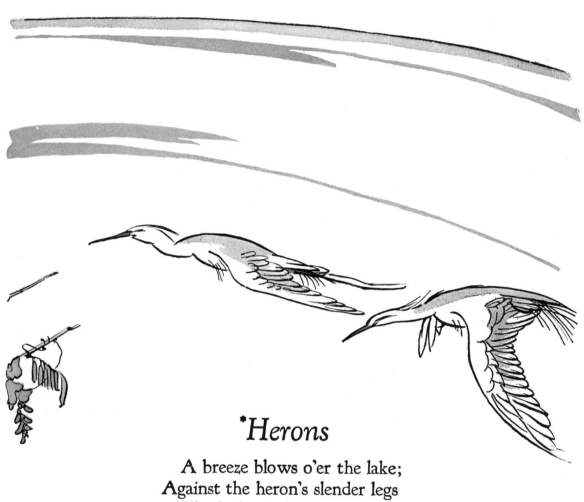

*Herons

A breeze blows o'er the lake;
Against the heron's slender legs
The little ripples break.

Buson

If they had no voices, lo!
White herons would be
But a line of snow.

Sokan

【37】

*The Cuckoo's Song

Was that the cuckoo's song?
I needs must stop! My tow-rope slacks,
The boat just drifts along.

Josui

Watching for Wild Geese

Since I faintly heard,
Far away, the first wild goose
Give forth his cry,
My thoughts have been fixed only
On the middle of the sky.

Misune (about 900 A. D.)

*Bamboos in the Moonlight

Between the bamboos tall
The moonlight softly trickles,
And I hear the cuckoos call.

Bashō

No Oil for my Lamp

No oil for my lamp,
And so I go to bed tonight;
But lo! the moon to give me light!

Bashō

Beneath Pear Blossoms

See by the moon's pale light,
A maiden strolls 'neath the blossoming pears,
And reads a note tonight.

Buson

Wild Goose or Wild Swan?

That which yonder flies,—
Is it a wild goose? Is it a swan?
If it be a wild goose,
Its name I shall soon tell you;
If it be a wild swan—ah, that is better still!

Sparrows and Hawks

Hawks are out and sparrows say:
"Let plums go hang for all we care!
We will not venture out today!"

Yaha

*Swallows

The swallows in their nest,
That twitter in the early dawn,
Disturb my morning rest.

The Stork

Hello, you storks, you shouldn't cry,
Returning there so safe and sound,
Home across the sky.

Issa (1763-1827)

〖 43 〗

*The Owl

The midday sky, no doubt,
Is one thing that the owl has quite
Made up its mind about.

*The Kingfisher

The kingfisher today
Uses the lake as looking-glass
To plume his wings so gay.

The Woodpecker

What, with all the flowers in bloom,
The woodpecker still has eyes to see
Nothing but a withered tree!

Jōsō

The Duck

The little duck looks very wise
When he pops up fresh from the sight
Of what below the water lies.

Jōsō (1663-1704)

The Pheasant

Long dragging like the mountain trail,
The feathers of the pheasant's tail.

The Pheasant and the Cock

The bird of the moor, the pheasant, cries;
The bird of the yard, the cock, crows.

Little Lady Moon

No-no-san,
Little Lady Moon,
How old are you?
I'm thirteen days;
I'm thirteen days and nine.
You're young then, Moon!
That is why you wear
That bright red sash
That only children wear,
And have that fine white girdle
Wrapped about your hips.
Will you give your girdle to the horse?
   Oh no, no, no!
Will you give your girdle to the cow?
   Oh no, no, no!

*The Firefly Lights his Lamp

Although the night is damp,
The little firefly ventures out,
And slowly lights his lamp.

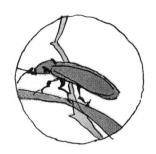

*Fireflies in the Water Weeds

Fireflies in the gloom
Among the water weeds, are like
The water weeds in bloom.

*Fireflies at Daybreak

The hours flit fast away,
The firefly hides his tiny lamp
At the approach of day.

*Poppies

O winds of Heaven, pray,
A moment calm your tumult,
For the poppies bloom today.

*Crocuses

The sunrise tints the dew,
The yellow crocuses are out,
And I must pick a few.

The Morning Glory

So soon I shall be gone,—
I'm but a morning glory,
A fleeting face-at-dawn.

Moritake (1472-1549)

[48]

*Iris

Ere yet the sun is high,
All blue the iris blossoms wave,
The color of the sky.

*The Lily Princess

Down from her dainty head
The Lily Princess lightly drops
A spider's airy thread.

*Daffodils

In spite of cold and chills
That usher in the early spring,
We have the daffodils.

*The Frog and the Cherry Petal

A petal lightly dropped
Upon the mouth of Mr. Frog,
 And now his song has stopped.

Riūkio

The Dragon Fly

A stem of grass,
 Whereon in vain,
A dragon fly attempts to light.

Bashō

*Moths

The moon is clouded o'er,
And soon the moths will sally forth
To dance upon the moor.

Jōsō (1663-1704)

Ants in the Rain

Alas, the poor thing has nowhere to go!
How sad for the homes of the ants
Is this fifth month when it's raining so!

*The Little Fly

Wet with the evening rain,
A little fly with heavy wings
Crawls slowly up the pane.

[51]

*Foxes Playing

The moon is shining bright,
And 'round my white narcissus beds
The foxes play all night.

Buson (1716-1783)

The Tom-Cat

Having no sweetheart, the tom-cat, ah me!
Gazes sadly at the sky,
And sings so mournfully.

Kyorai (1651-1704)

*Rabbits and Chestnuts

Where can the rabbits play
In safety from the chestnut burrs
That fall so fast today.

Seibe

*The Little Fawn

The fawn so light and slim
Finds that the low green creepers make
A lovely bed for him.

Yaha (1663-1740)

Colts

Colts behind their mothers
Trot across the plain,
Rustling, zoro-zoro, like a lady's train.

*Cattle

How cool the cattle seem!
They love to swish their tails and stand
Knee-deep within the stream.

Bankō

A Horse Race

A horse race? 'Tis the sound
Of rushing hoofs that gallop past,
And barely touch the ground.

Kōdō

The Last Rider

Alack! 'Tis sad indeed to see
The rider who has lost the race
Still struggling gallantly.

〖 55 〗

The Crescent Moon

The winds blow high;
A crescent moon floats into the clouds,
And drives them across the sky.

The Shark and the Crescent Moon

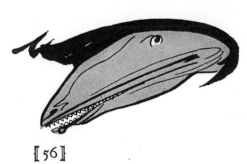

The crescent moon gives slender light,
Yet reason enough for the shark
To hide his head tonight.

Starlight

"Ko-ko, ka-shi-ko,"
  The frogs begin to shout,
  And evening stars come out.

Kikaku (1661-1707)

What the Frogs Say

"Let day pass,
  Let night dawn!"
So sing the frogs morning and evening.

Buson

The Bats

The bats are flitting, look!
Down in the gloom beneath the bridge
Above the gurgling brook.

Shibō

[57]

Prince or Fox?

Is that a gallant prince who yonder goes? Why, nay!
'Tis a masquerading fox charmed forth to play
Beneath the misty moon of May!

Buson

A Weasel in the Clover

By the temple 'tis time of dusk,
Who-is-it?-time! Too dark to see!
A weasel peeps from the clover and asks, "Who is it?" of me!

BUSON

Setting Out Rice Plants

O muddy water, would that you were clear,
To serve as mirror for the girls
Who plant the rice fields here.

Singing in the Fields

Though I hear the voice of my beloved
Singing in the fields,
I cannot see her.
She is hidden from me,
Like a grasshopper in tall grass.

My Darling Boy

Oh, they have sent him to the rice field!
  When I think about him,—
    When I think,
    When I think,
  When I think about him.
I—do nothing at all;—
  Even on this spring day,
    Even this spring day,
    Even this spring day,
  Even on this spring day.

The Moon Shining through the Rain

June rains, and through the pines,
Creeping out as if by stealth,
Lo, one night the old moon shines!

Ryota (1719-1787)

The Moon with a Halo

Gentle moon, come forth again,
Come now, even in the rain;
Put on your big umbrella-hat!

The Moon's Reflection in the Sea

The moon reflected
In the sea,
Though washed by waves
That rise and fall,
Is still as lovely as can be.

Tukayabu (900-930)

The mirrored image of the moon shall be
A pillow for the bird that floats
Asleep upon the sea.

【63】

Daybreak in Summer

A lovely morn! The summer night is gone;
How hushed and still is all the world
In wonder at the dawn.

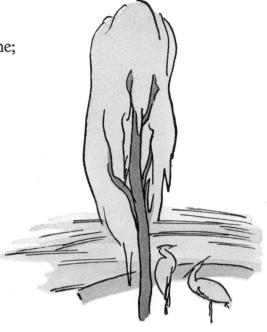

A Little Pool

The summer breezes blow,
And part the leafy greenery
To show the pool below.

Green Leaves in the Sunlight

Ah, how sublime—
The green leaves, the young leaves
In the light of the sun!

Bashō

*Fish in the River

Fish in the river rise
This peaceful summer day and snap
At little dragon flies.

Clouds

A summer room,
Where lying down,
I see the clouds as they go past.

Yaha

Clouds and Poppies

Red poppies down below,
And overhead, across the sky,
White clouds that go drifting by.

〖65〗

A Country Lane

Summer showers have passed again,
And hidden deep in flowers
Is every country lane.

*Midges Humming

When summer showers pass,
The midges hum upon the moor
Above the meadow grass.

The Brook and the Willow Tree

Poor lonely willow tree,
With nothing but the bubbling brook
To keep it company!

A Mountain Brook

Bubbling among the stones,
The little mountain rivulet
Its morning prayer intones.

*A Summer Scene

As through the fields I pass,
A summer parasol appears
Above the waving grass.

A Maiden

Is it a flower? Is it a butterfly?
Butterfly or flower?
When you come flickering like that, you charm me.
When you come twinkling like that, I am bewitched.

The Skylark

O Skylark,
For whose bubbling song
The livelong day is not too long!

Bashō

Left in their nest alone,
The young ones long for her return,—
Too high the lark has flown.

Sampū

*When voice and wings need rest,
The little skylark from the sky
Drops down into her nest.

Sea Gulls

A troop of sea gulls, pretty sight,
And lo! a gust of wind off shore,
That breaks their whirling flight.

The Crane

The white crane standing,
I thought to be a wave,
Driven by the wind
Upon the river's shore,
That, caught there, could roll back no more.

Emperor Uda (889-897)

The Little Maid-Servant's Complaint

After I've swept and tidied all,
Adown some more camellias fall!

O to be Tree-man

O to be tree-man,
Singing songs given back by the winds,—
What joy of no-man!

The Sunflower

A rainy day in June, yet see,—
The sunflower turns its face
Toward the spot where the sun should be.

Pinks

O gentle breezes, as you go,
Come with perfume of the pines,
Upon my pinks to blow!

Peonies

When spring gives place to summer days,
Men turn their thoughts again to praise
The peony.

The White Lotus

The great white lotus is in flower,
And very sad the bees must be,
To leave it at the sunset hour.

Orchids

Orchids are in bloom;
Like incense clouds wafted by butterflies' wings,
Is their perfume.

Lilies

I thought I saw white clouds, but no!—
Bending across the fence,
White lilies in a row!

Shikō (1665-1731)

The Modest Violet

 Climbing this mountain pathway,
No lovelier flower I see
Than that shy little violet, hiding modestly.

Bashō

The Forward Thistle

The thistle, thrusting himself into view,
To be seen by strangers that pass,
Got himself noticed all too well,
And was eaten by an ass!

Bashō

〖 77 〗

Go Away, Friend Cricket

Let me sleep, I pray!
Go away, friend Cricket;
Go away!

Issa

A Frog in Battle

Poor little frog, so lean and thin,
Fight on and don't give in,—
Issa is with you.

Issa

The Battle of the Flea

I dreamt last night
   I was a hero pierced in fight,—
How sharply fleas can bite!

Kikaku

Noise and More Noise

The boatmen's noisy quarrel is o'er;
Alack, but here's more noise, and more,—
   The frogs!

Yūya

A Boy Cutting Grass

O boy cutting grass
Over there on the hillside,
  Do not cut like that.
I want the grass to grow
  For the honorable horse
Of my lord who will soon come.

Hitomaro

A Lady Crossing a Bridge

Fair lady, tripping across yon bridge
Over the foaming river bed,—
Dress of scarlet, robe of blue,
Crossing a lacquered arch of red,—
Tell me, as you go alone,
Have you a husband waiting at **home?**

Lords and Ladies

The men have gone off
To the honorable hunt.
The ladies are seen
Trailing their red petticoats
Across the sea-beach clean.

Akahito

Call back your Dog

Call back your dog!
He's scratching through my hedge
    As you pass by to hunt, my lord.
In the leaf-thick shade
    Of this green mountain side,
Pray rest your horse, my lord.

*The Mikado's Bow

When day is come,
He takes his bow and fondles it with pride;
When day is done,
He lays it on his pillow by his side.
Hark to the twanging of the string!
This is the bow of our great Lord and King!
He rides forth to the chase at break of day,
At evening once again he rides away.
Hark to the twanging of the string!
This is the bow of our great Lord and King!

Hashibito

*This Mikado was Zhiyomei, who died 641 A. D.

**A Prince Hunting*

When our prince, the mighty monarch,
When our prince, of high-set splendor,
To the hunt with many a horseman,
Marches o'er Kariji's moorland,
Kneeling low, the deer adore him,
Kneeling low, the quail surround him.

Hitomaro

*This Prince was Prince Ossa, the son of Emperor Temmu,
who died 715 A. D.

An Emperor on the Rooftop

Up to my high roof I climb,
And when I look about,
I see smoke rising.
The kitchens of the people
Are flourishing, no doubt.

Emperor Nintoku (313-399)

An Emperor in a Poor Reaper's Hut

At rice-harvest time
I watched in a reaper's hut the long night through.
Alack! so weakly built it was, so thinly thatched,
　　My sleeves were drenched,—
Was it with tears of pity or with the autumn dew?

Emperor Tenchi (7th Century)

Little Fishing Boats

How gladly would I spend my days forevermore
Watching the little fishing boats,
All rowing up the bay toward shore,
And drawing in their nets with long, curved ropes.

Tukayabu

The Fisherman

Off the Cape of Isora
   Even the fisherman catching fish,
   Even the fisherman catching fish,
Works for the sake of the one he loves
   Even the fisherman catching fish,
   Even the fisherman catching fish.

He Who Sailed Away

O fisher's boat,
Tell men of me.
    Tell them I sailed away
Into the eighty isles,
Into the bluest field, — the sea!

In Morning Mists

Off Akashi's shore,
Dim, dim, in the morning mists,
    By islands hid from me,
Plies the boat I'm thinking of,
That bears my lord to sea.

Hitomaro

[[89]]

The Dragon-City of Elfland

In the harbor at ebb-tide, lo!
The shell-fish casts his spell to show
The tiny image of Shinkirō,
The Dragon-City.

The Maiden-Princess

When the shell-fish breathes his magic spell,
Elf-land appears;
Then all can clearly see
The Maiden-Princess
Of the Dragon-Palace.

[91]

Mount Fuji

Around a turn, and suddenly
There against the autumn skies,
Behold the mighty Fuji rise!

Onitsura (1661-1738)

Mt. Fuji's Snow

To Taga in Suruga-land, I'll go,
Down by the water's edge,
To see on great Mt. Fuji's height
Whiter far than utmost white,
The freshly fallen snow.

Akahito

A Flowery Moor

What a flowery moor, ah me!
Up great Fuji-yama's slope
Stretching pleasantly.

Ransetsu

Snail Climbing Mt. Fuji

The snail does all he can,
But ah, it takes him quite a while
To climb great Fuji San!

Issa

〖 93 〗

Fishing With Cormorants

With smoke the flaming torches soil
The faces of the fishermen,
Through their long night of toil.

〖94〗

*An Early Morning Scene

The murmur of the sea,
And showing through the morning mist,
A single Torii.

Kikaku

*Mists of Daybreak

The mists of daybreak seem
To paint as with a fairy brush
A landscape in a dream.

Buson

⟦95⟧

*Buddha

Above the lotus pond
The image of great Buddha stands
His gaze fixed far beyond

The Temple Bell

The cuckoo sings to tell
The little temple anchorite
To ring the morning bell.

A temple on a hill,
And now at dawn when all is still,
A startling bell that wakes the rooks!

Yayū (1702-1783)

The butterfly sleeps well,
Perched on the temple bell,
Till clang, it rings!

〖97〗

A Song of the Temple

When I visit the honorable temple I see the august gate;
I find the august gate to be of silver, its panels of gold;
Noble indeed is the gate of the honorable temple,
     The honorable temple!

When I visit the honorable temple I see the garden;
I see young pine trees flourishing everywhere;
On the first little branch of one the tomtit has made her nest,
     Has made her nest!

When I visit the honorable temple I see the water tank;
I see little flowers of many colors set all about it,
Each one having a different color,
     A different color!

When I visit the honorable temple I see the parlor room;
I find many kinds of little birds gathered all together,
Each one singing a different song,
     A different song!

When I visit the honorable temple I see the guest room;
There I see the priest with a lamp beside him,
Reading behind a folding screen;—how admirable it is,
     How admirable!

A Lantern Dance

All night long the dance goes on,
Till dew upon the dancers' sleeves
Proclaims that it is dawn.

Lanterns

The lantern on that post,
Has dropped asleep tonight,—
It must be that the dew has just put out its light!

It has gone out,—
My lantern's last small spark,
And left me here alone,—alone to face the dark!

The Moon Ship

In the ocean of the sky,
Borne on rising waves of cloud,
The moon ship
Goes a-gliding by
Through a forest of stars.

Hitomaro

Moon Gazers

The moon is at its best tonight;
Therefore we thank the clouds that o'er it flit,
And let us rest our necks a bit.

Bashō

A Wish

O moon, if born again, I'd be
A pine tree on a mountain's peak,
That when you rise I might be first to see.

Tree Shadows

All hushed the trees are waiting
  On tiptoe for the sight
Of moonrise shedding splendor
  Across the dusk of night.
Ah, now the moon is risen,
  And lo, without a sound
The trees all write their welcome
  Far along the ground!

Why the Cuckoo Sings

The one I love
Must, I think, have climbed
    The summer mountain yon,
And that is why the cuckoo
With a louder note sings on.

Akimine (9th Century)

I Like You

Although I saw you
The day before yesterday,
    And yesterday and today,
    This much is true,—
I want to see you tomorrow, too!

Masuhito (8th Century)

My Children

I never eat a melon,
    But I think of my children;
I never eat a chestnut,
    But I think of my children;
Tonight I cannot even sleep,
    I'm thinking so much of my children!

The Nightingale and the Dinner Gong

The nightingale begins his song,
But in the house the family
Hears—the dinner gong!

Buson

Human Nature

When it's summer, people say:
"Would that winter were here today!"

Onitsura

Obsequious Mr. Courtier Frog

Like a humble courtier
Fallen flat with hands upon the floor,
The frog croaks flatteries evermore.

Don't Be a Frog

Who wants to be a frog,
Opening his great mouth so wide,
He shows his whole inside?

Heat

How hot it is!
Scarce can I bear
To have the child upon my back play with my hair!

*A Hot Night

O summer moon, we pray,
Open the wind-bag of the gods,
And let the breezes play.

Locusts Hissing

In the hour of heaviest heat,
How the forest simmers
With the hissing of locusts.

Hear that shrill soft hissing.
Is it the dew that's come to life?
No, it's only the locust singing,—
min-min-min dzzzzzzz.

A Stormy Sunset

Angry fire of setting sun,
A sky banked up with clouds,—
Alack, this peaceful day is done!

A Clap of Thunder

Above and all around
The thunder rolls, and poppies drop
Their petals on the ground.

Lightning

A flash of lightning bright!
Then darker, darker than before
The blackness of the night!

Leaves are Falling

The leaves are falling;
In the house one cannot tell,
As they go drop, drop,
Whether rain is falling,
Or whether rain is not falling.

Minamoto no Yorizane (c 1220)

*Fairies

The fairies, it is said,
Drop maple leaves into the streams
To dye their waters red.

Kikaku

*A Carpet

The storm last night has laid
A coverlet of maple leaves,
As gay as red brocade.

〖112〗

*Girls in a Garden

Skirts trailing in the dew,
The girls around the garden stroll,
The autumn tints to view.

[113]

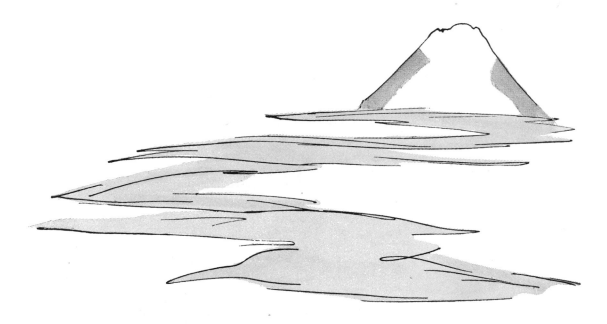

The Mountain in the Sky

River fog has risen high,
  Hiding the base of the mountain.
Lo, the autumn mountain looks
  As though it hung in the sky.

Kiyowara Fukuyabu

*Sunset

The crimson sunset glow
Is on the mountain, on the mist,
And on the sea below.

A Peaceful Autumn Morning

An early morning breeze;
Yes, and a single goose
Up in the white clouds, nothing more.

Bashō

Spiders' Webs

The mist is gone,
And on the meadows spiders' webs
Are glistening in the dawn.

Hakuyū

Dewdrops

Silver dewdrops
That in autumn light upon the moor,
Are jewels, I believe.
See how they're hanging everywhere
On threads the spiders weave.

Asayasu

Woodcutters

Dusk has come again
To the woodcutters' track
As past my hut it threads;
I hear the voices of mountain-men
Going down to the sheds.

Smoke

On Kasuga's moor
The rising of smoke is seen;
Surely the women
Must have picked lettuces,
And are boiling them on the green.

Hitomaro

[117]

Autumn Rain

Patter of the rain,—
All the brooks a-gurgling:
  "Autumn's here again!"

Fields of Ripened Rice

Can I be dreaming?
It seems but yesterday
  We set the little rice plants out.
Yet now the autumn winds are blowing,
And fields of yellow rice are showing.

Chrysanthemums and Butterflies

Chrysanthemums in bloom today,
Colors like a paint dish gay,
Come, butterflies, come here and play!

Ransetsu

White Chrysanthemums

Prisoned moonbeams
Caught in early frost,
Lo, white chrysanthemums!

Dew

If the white dew
From my chrysanthemums cool
Were to drip each day,
How many ages would it take
To collect and make a pool?

Kiyowara Motosuki (907-990)

Dew

Are the fallen stars
Returning up the sky?
No, the dew is on the grass.

*Tea Flowers

Tea flowers and cloudless skies;
The air is still, not e'en a breath
From wings of butterflies.

Rito

A Butterfly Picture

See that butterfly
On the woman's path,—now fluttering
Behind her, now before!

Quaint Fancy

I thought I saw the fluttering leaves arise,
Returning to their branches;
Lo, 'twas only butterflies!

Arakida Moritake (1472-1549)

Little Butterfly

O little butterfly,
With wings still moving
Even when it lights!

⟦ 121 ⟧

Would I Could Fly

How hard it is to cross the plain,
With tangled bamboo grasses high;
Alack, we struggle along on foot!
Would we could fly through the sky!

Junks in a Squall

What haste!
A sudden squall,
And sails set straight and sails set slant!

Kyorai

Autumn Winds

Though it does not show
Plainly to my eyes as yet,
　　Autumn's come, I know;
I am alarmed because
The wind is blowing so.

Fujiwara no Toshiyuki (d 907)

*Cold Wind

The autumn wind is bleak;
It whitens as with powder puff
My little baby's cheek.

Be Kind, O Wind

It was so thin,
The dress my brother wore.
O wind from Sao,
Pray don't blow hard
Till he comes home once more.

Lady of Sakanoye

One Who Cares

I wish I could lend a coat
To my Lord, who is going
Over the hill of Sanu,
Through the cold morning breath
Of the autumn wind that is blowing.

Akahito (c 730)

Lonely and Deserted

Some water fowls,
And in the midst of withered trees,
Two palanquins left alone.

Buson

A Desolate Scene

The end of autumn
And some crows
Perched upon a withered branch.

Bashō

Hobgoblins

Look, the old goblin his very self!
Aye, see there the bogie pass!
Nay! 'Tis only withered grass.

Yayū

The Voice of the Deer

In this mountain village,
Deep in the night I hear,
When the wind in the rice leaves wakes me,
Hark, the voice of the deer!

Morotada (c 1050)

The Deer on the Mountain

Living on the mountain of evergreens, the deer
Has no autumn leaves
To tell him when autumn's here!
He'll know it only
By his own cry, I fear!

Yoshinobu (c 990)

Cry, O Crickets

Cry, cry, O crickets
Of the wooded hill;
Full well I know
Why you chirp so mournfully,—
You're sad to see autumn go!

Yoshitada

Rats and Camellias

Rain drips down on the garden beds,
And scurrying rats are dragging off
The fallen camellia heads.

A Hare in a Hail Storm

The hail comes beating down;
A frightened hare bursts from the reeds
And dashes o'er the ground!

Come, Use Your Wits

One would think you came
From the island of Uruma, a place
Where they speak no Japanese,
When you make that face,
As though you cannot understand my words.

Sokan (1465-1553)

Catching a Thief

I've caught a thief! Bring lights to see!
Who is it I've trapped so cleverly?
Why now alack, 'tis my own son!

Kinto (966-1041)

*An Untimely Visitor

Alas! My fire is out,
And there's a shadow on the wall,—
A visitor, no doubt!

Bashō

A Visitor

Some one at my door, I pray?
Go away! O go away!
Good night, sir or madame!

Over the Bridge of Seta

How many people hurrying go
Through the drizzle to and fro,
Over the Bridge of Seta!

Jōsō (1663-1704)

A Traveler Caught in a Storm

Across the storm-swept plain
The rider urges on his horse,
In squalls of wind and rain.

Kiokusui

A Hurricane

A moment's stillness
Mid the hurricane's wild roar,
But Oh, the waves keep dashing up high upon the shore!

Gensui

Moon of the Mountain Fringe

Out of the dark,
Into a dark path
I now must enter!
Shine on me from afar,
Moon of the mountain fringe.

A Warrior at Nightfall

Night's come,—I've lost my path.
I'll take my lodging here beneath this tree;
So shall the mountain cherry flowers
Tonight play host to me.

A Traveler

As I make my
Traveler's bed on the rocks,
   I'm cold tonight!
Would the rocks might lend me
   Their moss-garments light!

Komachi (834-880)

Traveler in the Cold

If the frost should fall
On the moor, where we travelers
   Tonight will lie,
Enfold us, who are your children,
   With your wings, O crane-flocks of the sky!

*Snow

The snow fell in the night,
And people rouse each other up
To see the lovely sight.

Ransetsu

Off We'll Go

Off we'll go
To see the snow,
Till we take a tumble!

Bashō

*Willows in the Snow

The willows hanging low,
Shake from their long and trailing skirts
The freshly fallen snow.

Tsūrū

Snow Blossoms

When the snow falls,
Behold each bush and tree,
 Till then fast bound by winter,
Breaks forth into such blossoms
As in spring we never see.

Winter in the Sheltered Land

Winter's come once more
Even to my cottage door,
    As it lies hid from view,
Here amid the rush-leaves
In the sheltered land of Tsu.

Minamoto no Shigeyuki (d 1000)

No Eyes for Beauty

A glorious moon in winter,
But my Oh's and Ah's I check,—
I'm more concerned with drawing
My scarf about my neck!

Sampū (1648-1733)

*Footprints in the Snow

As men pass to and fro,
Their footprints mar the beauty of
The pure unbroken snow.

Yayū

Marring the Snow

If he for whom I've waited
Should still come,
  What shall I do, alack!
Across the fresh snow of the garden
He'll be making a track.

Shikibu

The Pine Tree

Lo!
Fresh and green amid the snow,
A pine-tree.

A Winter Scene

The heavy winter snows
Have capped with white the pine-tree tops
Where sleep the big black crows.

*Hoar-frost

This bright and sunny morn,
The hoar-frost jewels flashing bright
My cottage thatch adorn.

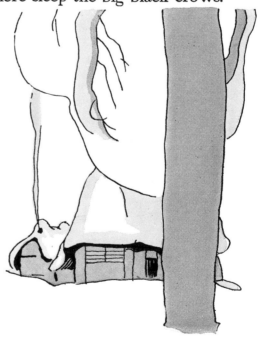

The Snow-Woman

She has vanished at break of day;
Whither she's gone, no one can say!
Now that which seemed to be
A snow-white woman,
Behold, is but a willow tree!

As for the Snow-Woman,
If I am not mistaken, even her best comb
Is made of ice;
And probably her hairpin, too,
Is all of ice.

Hailstones

Oh, would this sparkling hail might fall
    Until the moon shall rise!
'Twould shine and glisten then like gems,
    Like diamonds from the skies.

*Hail on the Pine-Trees

The hail falls pitterpat,
And fiercely rattles down upon
The brave old pine-tree's hat.

Bashō

Snow Alight

The sun shines bright;
Almost you'd think its fire
Had set the snow alight.

Morning School

The morning's cold and now begin
Loud rappings at the schoolroom door;
My boys are seeking to get in!

Taigi

*My Little Sword-Bearer

Where is the boy? Hallo!
The little lad who bears my sword
Has tumbled in the snow!

Shigen

The Fishman

The fishman! Oh, pray call him back!
He's vanished in the storm, alack!

The Rag Picker

Through winter's first cold snow,
See the poor shivering rag-man go,—
Yet he, too, is a son of man.

Ransetsu

【 147 】

*An Image on the Moor

Far from the busy town
This Buddha stands, and from his nose
An icicle drips down.

Issa (1763-1827)

The Snow and the Mill Wheel

The busy snow, fast falling on the ground,
Collects upon the mill wheel
And tries to turn it 'round.

The Mill Wheel

If the mill wheel please
To keep on turning busily,
The water has no time to freeze.

Keiriu

A Snow Storm

O snowstorm clouding the sky,
At your blast o'er sea and hill
  The birds begin to cry.

Chigetsu

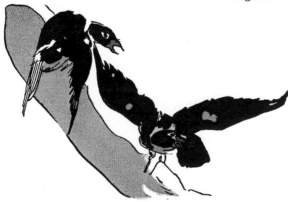

A Mountain Village
in the Snow

To this mountain village,
With its roads all buried
  Deep in snow,
  No one has come
Before me, I know!

Fujiwara no Tsunehira (c 1200)

A Runaway

My pony's tracks
Are buried deep in the snow.
Those from whom I fled,
Left far behind, will wonder
Which way they ought to go.

Saigyō Hoshi (1118-1190)

The New Year's Here Again

The New Year's here again,
    With joy among men,
And what a chattering of sparrows!

Ransetsu

*The old year's passed away;
The capital from end to end
    With flowers and lights is gay.

New Year's Callers

'Tis New Year's day,
　　And Last Year's Bills drop in
Their compliments to pay.

Important Little Johnny

Lo, how big feels Johnny here,
Come in his father's name to present
Good wishes for the coming year.

Yaha

Of Lovely Things in Japan

FAR away toward the sunrise, in the blue waters of the Pacific, lies the Empire-of-Myriad-Islands, the Land-of-the-Dragon-Fly, Japan. In Japan there is wealth of sunshine, of flower-bloom, and of bird-song, and the people love these beautiful things. They love trees and breezes, butterflies and birds, moonlight and starlight, and they love these things so much that for hundreds of years they have been writing verses about them.

Anyone may write verses in Japan,—that is, anyone who listens with all his heart to the song of the nightingale among the flowers, to the voice of the frogs in a star-lit pool, and the music of the wind, singing in the trees. Little girls, little boys, men and women, grandfathers and grandmothers, all may write poetry in Japan, and they write about the things they love,—about birds and blossoms and butterflies, and the shadows of the clouds that go racing over the fields at noon-day.

They write little verses on pictures, on gaily em-
broidered screens, on cups and plates, on painted fans,
on towels, on handkerchiefs,—in fact, they write
verses anywhere! The farm-girls with bare legs and
wide straw hats, standing knee-deep in the muddy
water of the rice fields, make verses and sing them
as they work. Fishermen, fishing by the flaming light
of torches, with those queer birds, the cormorants,
make verses as they fish. Porters, trudging up to their
necks in the tall grass, with packs on their heads,
make verses as they trudge. In joy or sorrow they
make verses, verses, verses. Indeed, in no country
of the world are all the people taught so truly to love
poetry as in Japan, and they know quite well, these
little folk of the Empire-of-Myriad-Islands, that every
single thing that has life, nightingale, butterfly, bee
or flower, is always, somehow, making a poem of its
own.

The Little Boy and the Sparrows
ISSA (1763-1827)

ONCE upon a time, more than a hundred years ago, there was a little boy named Issa, and he was a lonely little fellow, for he had no mother. One day when he was five years old, he was wandering about the yard, when he came upon a nest of baby sparrows in a tree. The tiny creatures were all alone. They, too, had no mother. Issa's heart was filled with love and tenderness for the helpless little things. Perhaps they were lonely as he. So he said:

"You little sparrows,
Left without a mother, come I pray,
Come and play with me today."

And that was as beautiful and tender a verse as anybody in the whole wide world, big or little, could have written. For a hundred years it has been famous in Japan.

Of Poetry Picnics and Fireflies

IN Japan they sometimes have poetry picnics. When Master Sōgi has an especially fine flowering tree, a cherry perhaps, all pink with a wealth of bloom, he invites his friends to a party. There they come in their holiday robes and little, clattering wooden sandals. They walk about the tree and admire it, they drink in its fragrance, and tea is served to them under its branches. Then they sit down and begin to scribble on narrow, little slips of paper. By-and-by each one has written a poem in pretty Japanese characters, and after he has read it to the others, he goes and fastens it to a branch of the tree in honor of which the party was given.

That is pleasure enough, certainly, for one afternoon, but if the guests stay until nightfall it is possible that Master Sōgi will provide for them another lovely game, that they may enjoy the beauties of Nature still further. When it is quite dark he will let loose hundreds of captive fireflies in the garden, and as the pretty things flit here and there, showing their airy, elfin lights in the dusk, the guests will chase them hither and yon, over little bridges, in among the flowers, around the quaint stone statues, about the tea house. All the garden will be gay with flitting forms and silver laughter, till the fireflies lose themselves in the moon-beams.

Of Plum Blossoms

PLUM blossoms, pink or white, are very dear to the hearts of the people of Japan. The plum-flowers come before the snow is gone.

What though the snow may fall?
It makes no difference to the plums;
They blossom through it all.

Sometimes a beautiful plum tree will have on its gnarled boughs its own white blossoms side by side with tiny white blossoms of snow-flakes. Little O-Suki San, seeing her father's plum-tree in bloom, will come clattering out of the house and stand on tip-toe to pick a flower. When she has it in her hand, lo, all at once it melts away, for what has she plucked but a snowball?

So early in the spring does the plum-tree flower, before all other blossoms, that it is called, "the elder brother of the flowers."

Of Cherry Blossoms

BUT ah! it is the cherry-blossom that is most dearly loved in Japan. The cherry-blossom is the favorite flower, and the Japanese love it so dearly that it stands to them as a sign for Beauty itself. When the lovely pink petals begin to fall from the trees in the spring, they imagine that all Nature sorrows and sighs to see them go.

When cherry-blossoms fall,
So sorrowfully men sigh.
Who knows—perhaps the soft spring showers
Are tears of the sorrowing sky!

For fifteen hundred years, their august Highnesses, the Mikados of Japan, have had garden parties on the beautiful hills at Yoshino, when they are a cloud of pink in cherry-blossom time. As many as ten thousand people have thronged at once to that lovely spot—lords and ladies in splendid garments, common folk, too, swarming over the hillside—aye! even the poorest of men and women from the city slums come on foot, a pilgrimage of two hundred miles, living on rice and water by the way, just to view the blossoms.

Some one among all that great multitude, struck dumb by the beauty of the sight, once stammered in halting words:

"Oh this! Oh this!
I have no words! I can but say,
'Flower-mountain, Yoshino!'"

Another cried:

"I thought I saw a great white cloud, but no!
I looked again and lo!
'Twas blossoms fluttering down from Yoshino."

One year when the cherry trees were later than usual in flowering, a certain Emperor grew so impatient for the coming of the blossoms, that he gave orders for the great bell of the temple to be struck and drums to be beaten, to bid the trees begin to bloom —

Strike the great bell,
That it may tell
The cherry trees to bloom!

Of Poetry Contests

EACH January there is a national poetry contest in Japan. The Emperor chooses a subject for his people to write about, and then everyone in the whole land, rich and poor, old and young, may send in a poem. Each one hopes within his heart that his poem will be so good it may be read aloud at a great gathering of the people, for the best of these verses are carefully selected to be read in public on a gala day, and then printed in newspapers and magazines.

Of Little Girls' Names

THE very names given the little girls in Japan are like tiny poems. No Jane or Susan or Mary is there. Instead are little Miss Cherry-blossom, Miss Butterfly, Miss Chrysanthemum, Miss Branch-of-little-bells, Miss Flower-garden, Miss Bright-helper, Miss Morning, Miss Shining Dew, Miss Frost or Miss New Moon!

Of Little, Little, Little Things

NOW the Japanese people are never very tall. They live in little houses, and they like little things,—little, little, little things. They love to make tiny carvings and paintings so small that their figures can only be seen through a magnifying glass. They like to have the tiniest of wire cages in which they keep little singing insects instead of birds; and they can make a whole garden with growing trees and fish ponds wherein real, live fishes swim, all so small it could be set upon a tea tray! And so they make little poems too,—little, little, little poems,—hokku poems with a whole world of meaning all shut up in seventeen syllables,—just the flash of a picture as if a window had been suddenly opened upon some beautiful scene, and then as suddenly closed again,—just a flash, and all the rest left for him who hears, to imagine and to feel.

Like little dewdrops are these poems, no more in size than the tiniest drop of water, but ah! reflecting all the shine and color of the sun.

[163]

The Boy Under the Persimmon Tree
(Hitomaro, about 737 A. D.)

ONCE upon a time, twelve hundred years ago, there dwelt in Japan a certain warrior named Ayabe. Now Ayabe and his wife had no child of their own, but one day Ayabe went out into his garden, and what should he see standing there quietly under a persimmon tree but a splendid little child, a boy of more than mortal beauty.

In utmost astonishment Ayabe approached the little fellow and said: "Who are you, child, and whence come you?" To this the little fellow made answer: "No father or mother have I, but the moon and winds obey me, and in poetry I find my joy."

Ayabe was so charmed with the boy and his words that he called his wife out to see him. She came hurrying from the house and when she saw what her husband had found, she was no less pleased than he. So the two took the little fellow into their home, and brought him up as their very own son.

True, indeed, it proved as Hitomaro grew, that he was the friend of moon and winds. He knew what they said, the moon and winds,—he heard their secret voice, and turned it into poems of magic words, so that others, too, might understand.

When he came to manhood Hitomaro served the Empress and the Mikado. He traveled all over Japan with their son, the Prince, and became one of the greatest of Japanese poets. Only one other man of his time could equal him, and that was Akahito [720-750]. Said a wise man of his day: "It is impossible to place Hitomaro above Akahito, or Akahito above Hitomaro." The verses of Hitomaro and Akahito have come down to this very day in a famous old collection having the beautiful name, "Collection of Myriad Leaves."

As time went on, the poets of Japan came to be called Friends of Moon and Winds, and so they were in very truth, for these were the things they loved,—moon and winds, birds and blossoms, frogs and crickets, butterflies and bees. Their hearts were as full of wonderment and adoration before all that had life, as simple and loving, as the hearts of little children.

The Lad Who Cleaned the Garden Path

THERE lived once in Japan a poet named Rikiu, and he had a son named Shoan. One beautiful autumn day when the maple trees were a glory of red and gold, Rikiu invited some friends to the little tea-house in his garden. Now the old sages used often to gather together in this little tea-house, and sit there in silence, dreaming shadowy dreams to the musical accompaniment of the singing tea-kettle.

"Shoan," said the father, "clean the garden path for my guests." And he pointed to the path of stepping stones that led from the busy outside world with its noise and hurly-burly, to the little tea-house by the tall, gray granite lanterns, so quiet and still beneath the peaceful shadow of the mossy, age-old trees.

Off went Shoan obediently with a pail of water and a broom, and soon there he was sweeping and scrubbing away, sweeping and scrubbing. By and by Shoan returned to his father.

"Honorable father," said he, "I have finished the task you gave me."

Out went Rikiu to look at the garden path but when he saw what Shoan had done he frowned.

"Nay," said he, "you have not really cleaned the path for my friends. Understand me better and try again."

But Shoan did not understand his father at all. He hearkened to his words only with his ears, and hearkening with one's ears is all well and good, but still there are wit and fancy and imagination, too, with which to hearken when others speak, and of these lively inward ears Shoan made no use whatever.

He hearkened, like a dullard, only with the ears on either side of his head. So he set to work once more, sweeping and scrubbing, sweeping and scrubbing. By and by he came to his father a second time.

"Honorable father," said he, "I have finished the task you gave me."

Out went Rikiu as before to look at the path, and just as before, he frowned and said:

"Nay, you have not really prepared the path for my friends. Try again."

At this Shoan was even more perplexed. If he had looked up at the glory of the trees above him, perhaps they would have told him the secret. Perhaps they would have set him listening to his father's words with wit and fancy, too, but alas! he did not look up; he looked only at the path and his pail.

"Then I shall have to scrub still more thoroughly!" he said, and he swept and scrubbed, and scrubbed and swept till the stones were as clean as the pebbly bottom of a brook.

Now when Rikiu saw that, however often he repeated his command, Shoan intended to do nothing but sweep and scrub, scrub and sweep, he strode to the spot where his son was standing beside his pail and cried:

"Simpleton! Sweeping and watering are not true cleaning. I will show you what is to be done with the garden path." And he shook the maple trees so that their leaves fell and covered the ground. There on the path they lay, making a beautiful carpet, a splendid brocade of gold and crimson, lit by living splashes of sunlight.

"This is the real way of cleaning and preparing for my guests!" said Rikiu. But Shoan could only stand and look on, open-mouthed and wondering.

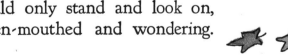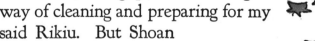

The Boy and the Moonlight

NOT so very many years ago there lived in Japan a boy named Yone Noguchi. On his way to school Yone used to pass through the beautiful pine forest of a famous park. Often as he walked, he would look with great longing toward a little cottage on a hill in this park. So tiny a cottage it was, that all of it might have been set down inside a western living room. Yet as it stood, perched up there on the hill, it was most inviting to Yone, for there lived an old poet named Yeiki. Now the boy admired this old man with all his heart and soul, and was eager to call upon him. Master Yeiki, he was sure, could open his eyes to many a secret of beauty that he was longing to know, but he hesitated to disturb him.

One night, however—it was the full moon of September—Yone set out through the park. He had made up his mind. He would call on Master Yeiki. As he walked along beneath the dusky pines, there were other wanderers beside himself abroad in the moonlight, moths, darting restlessly in and out among the shadows, as eager perhaps as he, to feel all the beauty of the night.

Up he climbed, and up. By and by he spied the house dimly through the trees. All was silent about it, and there was never a single light in a window.

"It is because the moonlight is so beautiful," said the boy to himself. "Master Yeiki wishes the moon to have full sway. He will not disturb it by lighting an earthly lamp."

On the doorstep, under the golden shower of the moonlight, loomed the dark figure of the old man.

Without a word, Master Yeiki rose, greeted his young guest and led him inside the house. There every door had been opened—opened to welcome the moonlight. With fairy-like, golden steps, that most honored guest from the skies, crept lightly, delicately into the room. Silently Yone and Master Yeiki sat down together. Time passed, the breezes whispered now and again, but no one else spoke a single word. By and by, by and by, the moon crept around to a point where it fell directly on the hanging beside the door. There its light suddenly brought out from the darkness certain words written in Japanese characters on the hanging:

> Autumn's full moon,
> Lo, the shadows of a pine tree
> Upon the mats!

The lad looked before him. There, sure enough, decorating the dustless mats by the door, splashed in splendor across their silver sheen, lay the dragon-shaped shadow of a pine tree!

It was the first time in his life that Yone had ever observed the full beauty of moonlight and shadow, and now it was the moon itself that had showed him. The secret thrilled him through and through, that beautiful secret revealed by the moon.

A little longer Yone stayed on in silence. Then he rose, bowed to Master Yeiki, and thanked him for a most interesting talk! A most interesting talk, and yet till now, neither one had said a word!

When the boy left the house he went down again through the pine forest. The moon was quite high now, and under its golden peace, trees and birds were sleeping. O, the beauty of night, and moonlight, and silence!

The Lady and the Morning Glory

(Chiyo, 1703-1775)

ONCE upon a time long ago, there lived a lady named Chiyo, and she had a little house, and a little garden, and a little well in her garden. One morning she went to her well to draw some water. But, ah me! what should she find there? Lo and behold, since last she came to that spot, a morning glory had twined its vine all about the rope that held the bucket,—gay little blossoms like bright little faces, climbing that rope, and nodding and smiling in all the joy of life!

Now what was to be done, pray tell? Chiyo had come there for water. Should she break those slender green tendrils, tear down those tiny acrobats from their airy swings, and draw up the bucket? No! ah, no! Too warm a tenderness filled her heart. A moment she stood, nodding and smiling back at the blossoms; then she turned away, leaving the rope to the little climbers. Off to a neighbor's house she must trudge with her pail, and when she reached there, this is what she said:—

> "The morning glory today
> Has taken my well-bucket away;—
> I come to beg for water, pray!"

When Master Poet Chuckled
Sōin (1605-1682)

NOW, though the old poets of Japan had so keen an eye for beauty, they sometimes liked to be funny, too. They laughed often and often, those old fellows, quietly perhaps, with not much more than a ripple of the face, but still they laughed. Here is a story of one of the things that seemed to them very funny.

Among the earliest white visitors to Japan, in the first half of the seventeenth century, were Dutch traders. The Dutch and all their customs seemed as queer to the Japanese, as the Japanese seemed to the Dutch.

"They are funny fellows, these white men," said the Japanese to themselves. And nothing seemed to them more comical than to think that white men wrote across the page instead of up and down. Up and down the page the Japanese wrote at that time, and up and down the page they write to this very day.

"Any ordinary, civilized person should write up and down, of course!" said they. And no little white boy could deem it funnier to see a Japanese letter with writing scratched all up and down, than they found it, to see a Dutchman's letter with characters written across it.

One day, a poet named Sōin saw a flight of wild geese, and noticed how they stretched out sideways across the sky. At that sight he began to chuckle, and by and by he wrote his chuckle down on paper. This is what he said:

Wild geese fly,
Sideways stretching, across the sky,
Like comical Dutch writing!

The Gentlest and Greatest Friend of Moon and Winds

Bashō (1644-1694)

ONCE upon a time there went wandering through Japan, sometimes on the back of a horse, sometimes afoot, in poor pilgrim's clothes, the kindliest, most simple-hearted of men—Bashō, friend of moon and winds. Though Bashō was born of one of the noblest classes in Japan, and might have been welcomed in palaces, he chose to wander, and to be the comrade and teacher of men and women, boys and girls in all the different stations of life, from the lowest to the highest. Bashō bathed in the running brooks, rested in shady valleys, sought shelter from sudden rains under some tree on the moor, and sighed with the country folk, as he watched the cherry-blossoms in their last pink shower, fluttering down from the trees. Now he slept at some country inn, stumbling in at its door at nightfall, wearied from long hours of tramping, yet never too tired to note the lovely wistaria vine, drooping its delicate lavender blossoms over the veranda. Sometimes he slept in the poor hut of a peasant, but most often his bed was out-of-doors and his pillow a stone.

When Bashō came upon a little violet hiding shyly in the grass on a mountain pathway, it whispered its secret to him.

"Modesty, gentleness, and simplicity!" it said. "These are the truly beautiful things."

Glistening drops of dew on the petal of a flower had a voice and a song for him likewise. "Purity," they sang, "is the loveliest thing in life!"

The pine-tree, fresh and ever green amid winter's harshest storms, spoke staunchly of hardy manhood; the mountains had their message of patience, the moon its song of glory! Rivers, forests, waterfalls, all told their secrets to Bashō, and these secrets that Nature revealed to him, he loved to show to others, for the whole living of life was to him one great poem, as of some holy service in the shadow of a temple.

"Real poetry," said Bashō, "is to lead a beautiful life. To live poetry is better than to write it." And whenever he saw one of his young students in a fit of anger, or otherwise acting unworthily, he would gently lay his hand on the arm of the youth and say:

"But this is not poetry! This is not poetry!"

Bashō and the Bees

THERE was never a little bee, or bird, or toad, but Bashō noticed and loved it. Once Bashō saw some bees hovering over the flowers in his garden. Nearby on a branch sat a sparrow, hungrily eyeing the pretty, buzzing things as though he meant to make a meal of them. And Bashō said tenderly:

"O sparrow, my friend, I pray
Do not eat the bees that hover
O'er my flowers today."

Bashō and the Toad

AGAIN, Bashō was out walking when he heard the croak of a toad. As he looked about to see whence the noise came, he found that the little creature was enjoying himself in fancied safety, under the very house of a man whose business it was to catch toads and sell their skins for the making of bags. Bashō could not pass by, without exclaiming:—

"A toad's croak! O take care!
Come hop away from there!
You're under the toad-catcher's house,—
beware!"

Bashō and the Dragon-fly

ONCE Bashō was riding along a country lane with one of his pupils named Kikaku. Kikaku was a warm-hearted, merry youth, but he was a little unruly, the bad boy among Bashō's students. As they rode, Kikaku spied a beautiful red dragon-fly darting before him, and he thought at once that the lovely creature, were it not for its wings, would look very much like a red cayenne pepper pod. So he made up a verse on the spot and said:

> "Pluck off the wings
> From a bright red dragon-fly, and see!
> There a pepper pod will be!"

But Bashō reined in his horse at once.

"That is not poetry!" he cried. "Do you call so cruel a thought as that, poetry? Plucking off the wings of a dragon-fly is not poetry. Instead of what you have just said, you should word your verse like this:

> "Add but wings
> To a bright red pepper pod, and see,—
> There a dragon-fly will be!"

The House That Burned Down

NOW Bashō had another student named Hokushi, whom he had taught to live poetry as well as to write it. Hokushi had a little house, a flimsy, little house made of wood and paper like many another house in Japan. One day his house caught fire. Hokushi stood by and watched the flames devour it. There was mad excitement everywhere, men running, shouting, crying.

"A man whose house is burning must feel sad and fearfully excited," said those who stood by.

But Hokushi remembered his master's teaching to keep a heart calm and serene whatever might happen. So he turned his eyes away from the burning house and lo! he saw pink blossoms falling from a cherry-tree nearby. Serenely they fluttered down, unhurried, calm and sweet in the midst of the hurly-burly. Hokushi's own heart as he watched them became as peaceful as the flowers. His house was burned to the ground, but he wrote of the matter thus to Bashō:

> "It has burned down;
> How serene the flowers in their falling."

When he received this little poem, Bashō at once called two of his students to him, and together they admired it.

"Hokushi did not study poetry in vain," said Bashō, "when his mind could keep serene like the falling flowers, while he watched his house burn to ashes. That is the real poetry!"

Bashō and the Rustics

ONE beautiful night Bashō passed on his travels through a certain little country village. The moon was full and so flooded earth and sky with light, that fields and houses stood out as clearly as at noonday. Now certain young men of the village had come out into the open air to enjoy the moonlight. They were sitting on the ground, eating and drinking, when all of a sudden they fell to making up verses about the moon. Bashō, perceiving this, stood by their circle to listen, delighted to find that even in a place so out of the way, these humble rustics loved the moon and made hokkus about it.

At length some silly youth in the party noticed Bashō.

"Why, there's a poor, beggarly sort of fellow," he thought to himself, noting Bashō's plain garments. "It will be great fun to set him making verses about the moon."

The young man, accordingly, suggested to his friends that they get the stranger to join them.

"It will be fine sport to hear what ridiculous things the poor beggar will find to say!" agreed the others, and they lost no time in inviting Bashō to join their party.

Bashō accepted their invitation readily, but he humbly took the lowest seat in the circle. Then the silly youth said further:

"Everybody here is bound to compose a poem about the moon. You must give us one, likewise, stranger."

At this, Bashō apologized.

"How can a poor countryman like me contribute to the entertainment of this honorable company?" he said. "I beg you to excuse me."

Thereupon the crowd of men grew all the more eager to hear him make himself ridiculous, so they shouted:

"No, no, no! We cannot excuse you! Good or bad, you must make up one poem at least!"

"Well," said Bashō at length, smiling and folding his arms. "Then I will give you one."

The young rustics could scarcely restrain their laughter, for anticipating their joke.

"'Twas the new moon," said Bashō.

"New moon!" snickered the silly youth to his neighbor. "What a simpleton the fellow is. He doesn't even notice that the moon is full, but gives us a verse about the new moon!"

"Let him go on," returned the other. "It will be all the more fun."

As to the rest of the party, they gathered about Bashō secretly snickering. Bashō, however, paid no heed. He merely went on with his poem:

> "'Twas the new moon!
> Since then I've waited—
> And lo, at last, tonight!"

The whole party was amazed at the exquisite beauty of the little poem. What could more perfectly and simply express the soul's deep and reverent joy, when the promise of the slender crescent in the sky is fulfilled at last in the longing hearts of men, by the matchless glory of a full moon? Abashed and humbled, the young men took their seats again, and said:

"Sir, you can be no common pilgrim to write such a remarkable verse. May we ask you your name?"

Thereupon Bashō smilingly replied:

"My name is Bashō, and I am traveling on a pilgrimage for the sake of practicing the art of poetry!"

In great excitement the rustics apologized for their rudeness to so great a man, "whose fragrant name," said they, "is known to all the world."

Basho forgave them, and the countrymen sent off post-haste for all their friends in the village to come out and join them. Then they began their feast anew, but this time in honor of Bashō.

Bashō's Home at Yedo

THERE was nothing that Bashō loved more than simplicity. Whenever he consented to live in a house at all, it was always in the humblest sort of a dwelling. For a time he had a tiny cottage in the garden of a friend at Yedo. His own little garden there was laid out with greatest care and in the center of it was a tiny pond. Often Bashō used to sit by this pond and think. As calm and still as the old pond were his thoughts, then all of a sudden, plop! a bright idea would flash across the quiet of his meditations, just like a frog, with sudden leap, springing into the water. One day as he sat there Bashō wrote a poem about this, the best known of all his poems.

> The old pond,—aye!
> A frog leapt into it,—
> List, the water sound!

Beside Bashō's house his students planted a banana tree. Now the word for banana in Japanese is Bashō. So the house soon came to be called Bashō-an or Banana House, and the master took his name from his house.

Once a friend visited Bashō at the Banana House. He found with the poet his two pupils, those high-spirited but devoted youths, Ransetsu and Kikaku. All three were living in a house of one room only and that room was eight mats, or twelve feet square. The sole furniture of the place was one pan and one kettle, and its sole ornament was a statue of the child Buddha, set in a hole in the wall. The boys had but one quilt as covering, and this they shared at night. It was so short, however, that it did not cover their feet, leaving their toes to stick out in the cold. Often they were kept awake by the cold, and when they could not sleep they would write poems like this:

> So cold am I,
> Awake, I lie.
> And, being awake, more cold am I!

For ten years Bashō and his pupils lived in this tiny cottage, devoted to one another. Then one day there was a great fire in Yedo. The cottage was burned to the ground and Bashō only escaped the flames by plunging into his pond. After that his pupils clubbed together to rebuild his cottage, but he would not go there to live. Instead, he started once more to wander, and never again lived in a house.

Bashō and the Rich Man

ONCE some rich and honorable people planned a great feast to do honor to Bashō. It was a very grand affair indeed. Hosts of servants served the guests with the richest of food. When it was over Bashō in his courtly, old-fashioned manner, thanked these friends for their kind intentions, but he added bluntly:

"Such feasting on rare and expensive food is nowise to my taste. One cannot feast like this and live poetry. When I need food I eat of the plainest. Nor will I accept your invitation to come here again unless I am entertained with perfect simplicity."

Fortunately, the rich and honorable people took Bashō's rebuke in good part. They begged him to come to their home again, and when he did so, nothing was provided for the guests but tea. This left plenty of time for talking of really important matters, and when their conversation was finished, it was Bashō himself who suggested that the company might be hungry and would like some cold rice. Thereupon, no servant, but the master of the house himself, brought in the rice, and in the family rice-tub at that! He helped each guest to a bowl or two of rice, with pickles as the sole ornament to the feast. The company gathered around in a circle to share the simple meal, and Bashō said warmly to his host:

"I thank you for the readiness with which you have agreed to my recommendation that you live plainly and think high thoughts!"

So in simplicity, gentleness, purity was the life of Bashō spent, and he remains to this day the greatest and best beloved of all the Friends of Moon and Winds.

The Herdboy and the Weaver

(A very ancient legend concerning the River of Heaven, the Milky Way. It has been the subject of numberless poems, the most beautiful of which are handed down from the "Collection of Myriad Leaves," gathered together in the Eighth century.)

THERE dwelt of old in the skies an Emperor of Heaven who had a beautiful daughter named Tanabata. Now Tanabata lived in a little house of her own on a star, and passed all her days in weaving shining garments for her august father, the Emperor. For years and years the maiden loved her work and rejoiced in it, and found no greater pleasure than weaving the gleaming sky-yarn into gleaming sky-garments. But one day as she sat before her loom at the door of her starry dwelling, Tanabata saw a handsome peasant lad pass by, leading an ox. The peasant lad looked at Tanabata, and Tanabata looked at the peasant lad, and straightway they loved each other. Then the heart of Tanabata grew unquiet. No more was she so joyous in weaving. She was thinking ever of the young herdsman, passing from star to star with his ox. By and by, Tanabata's father, the Emperor, guessed her secret and said to her:

"Daughter, since you think so much of that young lad, you shall have him for a husband."

Tanabata bowed to the blue floor of Heaven in gratitude to her august father. Hikoboshi, the herd boy, was summoned at once to the star and given permission to wed the little weaver of the skies. Happy indeed were the two and joyous was their wedding.

As time went on they proved to be more and more completely devoted to one another. But alas! so devoted were they, that they began to think only of themselves, of being always together. To sit hand in hand by the door of Tanabata's little house and talk with each other, or to walk hand in hand up the silvery path of the moon, picking the tiny star-flowerets that gleam like diamonds along the way, was all they thought of week in and week out. And so they fell to neglecting their duties, to doing less and less work, until at last they were doing no work at all. Tanabata spun no more garments for his honorable Augustness, the Emperor of Heaven. Hikoboshi paid no more heed to his ox, but let him wander untended over the boundless blue plains of the sky, grazing wherever he chose. Then was the Emperor of Heaven greatly displeased. He called the two before him and said:

"You have neglected your duties through caring only for one another. In punishment you shall be separated and live apart, with the River of Heaven flowing ever between you. Once a year from this time forward, and once a year only, shall you see each other. That shall be on the seventh night of the seventh month."

Thereafter, behold! It was even as the Emperor had said. The two were separated by the Milky Way, one on the right bank, one on the left, with the shining stream half hidden in mists, flowing ever between them. But Tanabata and Hikoboshi bowed their heads obediently to the Emperor's decree. It was just, they knew. And each went back to his work, she to

[184]

weaving before her door, he to guarding his ox. Patiently through long days they worked, looking forward to the autumn, when that happy night of their meeting should come.

Often during the year Tanabata went down to the reeds that grew beside the misty river, and looked longingly across. The little breezes could fly over the stream! The clouds could drift to that other side where her beloved lived. She only could not go. Then she would cry:

> "Though winds and clouds
> May freely come and go to either bank;
> Between myself and him, my husband far away,
> No message whatever may pass!"

Sometimes she took a pebble and threw it across the water, and in her longing she mourned like this:

> "To the opposite bank,
> One might easily fling a pebble;
> Yet, being separated from him by the River of Heaven,
> Alas, to hope for a meeting before autumn, is all in vain!"

Meanwhile, on the oposite shore, Hikoboshi came every night to the edge of the stream to look across and strain his eyes for a sight of his beloved. Through the five hundred layers of white cloud that hid her from him, he sometimes caught a glimpse of her. Then he sadly cried:

> "Though she is so near
> That the waving of her long sleeves
> Can be distinctly seen,
> Yet there is no way to cross the stream
> Before autumn."

Now when the long reeds by the river began to bend, to sway and sigh in the autumn breezes, then the lovers knew that the time for their meeting was near. Anxiously they hoped for a clear and starlit night. For, ah! only if it were clear could Hikoboshi cross in his little boat. If it should storm and rain, the River of Heaven would run too high, it would rush and roar, and swell into such a mighty stream that he could not possibly cross. In such a sad case the lovers would have to wait for another whole year to see each other.

At last it came, the long awaited night, calm and clear. Then Tanabata hearkened with all her soul for the first sound of oars in the River, and when she heard it, she cried:

> "On the River of Heaven,
>   At the place of the august ferry,
>   The sound of water has become loud.
>   My long awaited lord
>   Will soon be coming in his boat."

Quickly she ran down to the stream, so eager to see her young husband that she tripped far out into the shallow water, wetting her trailing skirt.

Ah, now she saw silvery spray rising in the distance and she knew it to be the spray from the oars of her beloved.

"He is coming!" she said. "My long-desired lord, whom I have been waiting to meet here on the banks of the River of Heaven."

Scarcely could she contain herself for eagerness. She needs must cry out to him:

"My not-often-to-be-met beloved,
O hasten to row thy boat across the River of Heaven!"

At length, out of the darkness, his little boat hove in sight. Tanabata saw him, young and strong, heedless of the silvery spray, rowing exultingly over the foaming stream. In a moment more he sprang to the shore by her side. O the joy of those two, the joy! What, though they might be together for only the brief space of twelve short hours? They were together, and that was enough.

So, all the year round, year in and year out, the Weaver and the Herd-boy wait in the heavens, ever young, ever eager, yet ever patient, performing their duties faithfully on either side of the Milky Way, and looking forward with longing to that one happy autumn night.

If there is rain on the seventh night of the seventh month, the people of Japan call it the rain of tears, because Hikoboshi can not pass over to his sweetheart, and they grieve with him in his sorrow. But if it is clear, and they see little white mists drifting over the Milky Way, they know that the mists are the spray from the Herdboy's oars, and they rejoice, crying: "There goes the Herdboy to visit the Weaver!"

For more than eleven hundred years one of the favorite festivals of Japan has been held on that night,—the Festival of Tanabata. Then it is the custom for people to write verses about the lovers, tracing the characters with freshly gathered dew on colored paper. They fix these little verses to bamboo poles and set up the poles on the roofs of their houses. Men and women, boys and girls, as they gaze at the shining stream in the sky, think of the Weaver at her starry loom, and the Herdboy waiting on the opposite shore. Then the heavens seem to them very near and warm and human, and the silence of night is filled with the dream of a tender, faithful, and patient love.

The Robe of Feathers

(Told from a classical, poetical drama of the Japanese)

'TWAS dawn in early spring, shell pink in a misty sky! Pale, new-born light gilded the tips of the pines on the shore, and the tips of the waves on the sea! Morning breezes sang in the pines, and, over all, towered Fuji-yama's snowy height!

Slowly, a little boat, dancing on the waves and glancing in the morning sun, drew in to the shore. A fisherman sprang to land. The fragrance of pines was in the air and blossoms came fluttering down. The fisherman raised his eyes and looked across flowery meadows to the snows on Fujiyama's peak. But ah, straight before him on a tree, behold! What snow was that he saw? No snow at all, but a beautiful thing hanging there on a branch, a thing of myriad softest lights rippling into one another, a thing of gleam and glimmer, a shining robe of feathers!

〖188〗

Quickly the fisherman seized the robe and took it down from the branch.

"'Tis wondrous beautiful!" he thought. "I'll take it back to the old folks in my village. I'll show it to all the villagers! A precious thing it will be, indeed, for them to stand and gape at. Aye, I'll keep it with care and hand it down to my children and children's children for many a generation."

Just then a lovely creature, a shining maiden, rose up out of the bright blue waters and stood on the shore before him, shedding a sparkle of silver drops.

"That robe is mine," said she. "Why have you taken it down?"

"I found it," said the fisherman, "and I shall carry it home."

"But 'tis a fairy's robe," the maiden answered anxiously, "a fairy's robe that mortals may not wear. I hung it there on the branch when I went to bathe in the sea."

"A fairy's robe!" cried the fisherman eagerly. "Now think of that! So you are a fairy?"

"Aye," said the maiden—"I am a moon-sprite, just flown down from the Palace of the Moon."

Ha, that was it! The fisherman understood. In the magic depths of the sky stands the Moon Palace, and within the gleaming silvery halls of the Moon Palace, a different King rules each day of the month. Fifteen Kings all robed in white reign for the first fifteen days, till the new moon hangs her sickle in the sky, then come fifteen kings in deepest black. And ever circling about each king with joyous songs is a band of happy sprites. One of these sprites was the maiden before him.

"If you are a fairy," said the fisherman, "then your robe is all the more valuable to me. I will not give it back! No! No! No! No!"

But the maiden began to entreat.

"Alas! without my robe of feathers I cannot fly. I cannot soar through the air and return to my beautiful home in the sky—I beg you, I beseech you, give it back to me."

"No!" cried the fisherman stubbornly. "I am more determined than ever. It will be indeed an adventure to carry a fairy's robe back to my village. I will not give it back!"

There were sobs now in the fairy's voice.

"Like a bird whose wings are broken, I cannot fly!" she cried.

"Aye", said the fisherman turning away. "You may well feel sad chained here to this dull earth when you used to fly so freely through the sky, but I will not give you back your robe!"

Alas, poor maiden! Tears like dew appeared on her eyelids. The very blossoms twined in her hair seemed to sorrow and droop. Gone was all her shine. Sadly she raised her eyes to the sky. There, half hidden by drifting mists, lay the well-known path from cloud to cloud, the path that led back home. Never again would she fly along that joyous way back to those silvery halls where her sisters played! High in the sky a crane was flying; over the ocean a sea-gull soared, mounting so freely on joyous wings. And the little breezes,—she heard them flying,—flying, flying over the plain.

"All these may fly! All these!" she cried. "The crane, the gull, the breezes. Only I—I alone shall never fly again."

So sad, so very sad was her cry, that pity stirred at last in the fisherman's heart. Slowly he turned about.

"Well then," he murmured, "I can but pity you. Take back your robe of feathers!"

"Oh joy! Oh joy!" cried the moon-maiden in an ecstasy of delight. "Then I shall return to my home in the sky."

"A moment, though!" cried the fisherman, still holding back the robe. "I will return your robe on one condition only. You must first dance for me one of those beautiful fairy dances, whereof I have often heard tell."

"Gladly will I dance," the moon-maiden said, "and moreover I will leave my dance behind me when I return to the skies, to show to mortals the art and grace of dancing. I will dance the most beautiful dance of the skies,— the dance-that-makes-the-Palace-of-the-Moon-turn-round. But first give me back my robe. I cannot dance without my feathers!"

"Nay, nay," said the fisherman. "If I give back the feathers you may fly away home to the skies and never dance for me at all."

"Fie on you! For shame!" cried the maiden. "I have promised to dance. Mortals may break their promises, but in heavenly beings there is no falsehood—no heavenly sprite could break her word."

"Tis true," said the fisherman. "You shame me, fairy maid. Here, take your freedom. Have back your robe."

In joy too deep for words the moon-maiden put on her beautiful robe. Blue as the sky it was, with wings all silvery white and soft like the mists of spring. At the first fluttering of those wings, they almost bore her away toward her beloved sky, but she held them here to Earth and began to sing:

"Heaven hath its joys; but there is also beauty here on earth.
 Blow, blow, ye winds, and drive the drifting clouds
 Across my path to bar my homeward way;
 I would not yet return unto the skies."

Then from the clouds came magic music,—lutes and tabrets, silvery flutes and tinkling cymbals. To these sweet strains the moon-maiden began to dance, her snowy pinions and the blossoms in her hair fluttering in the breezes. 'Twas a wondrous beautiful dance,—the dance-that-makes-the-Palace-of-the-Moon-turn-round. Such grace! Such lightness! Now here, now there! Swinging, swaying, twinkling in the light,—a rhythm, a harmony, a poetry of motion.

When the dance was finished, the breezes caught those magic wings. Lightly the shining maiden rose from the earth and rested a moment, poised and floating in the air. Then slowly her wings began to soar. Up and up they bore her, above the pine-clad shore and the bright blue sea, above the flowery meadows on Mt. Fuji's sides, higher, higher, higher, above the shining snow on Fujiyama's peak, higher, higher, higher, until at last, the drifting mists veiled her altogether from sight.

Then the fisherman stood on the shore alone.